M000205458

Sue Boettcher's
Black Cat Book

Souvenir Press

Copyright © 1990 by Sue Boettcher Black Cat illustrations and text
Copyright © 1990 Souvenir Press original design

First published 1990 by Souvenir Press Ltd,
43 Great Russell Street, London WC1B 3PA
and simultaneously in Canada
Reprinted 1990

All Rights Reserved. No part of this publication
may be reproduced, stored in a retrieval system,
or transmitted, in any form or by any means, electronic,
mechanical, photocopying, recording or otherwise without
the prior permission of the Copyright owner

ISBN 0 285 629972

Printed in Great Britain by
BPCC Hazell Books
Aylesbury, Bucks, England
Member of BPCC Ltd.

Did I hear someone getting up at last?

I don't believe a word of it.

This is definitely yesterday's milk . . .

. . . but that was certainly this morning's cream.

Now how did that happen?

I'm so bored . . .

. . . and I've read all these.

Not a lot happening here.

What's going on outside?

I'm tempted but I haven't got the energy.

I'll just sit here and look beautiful.

Where did you spring from?

I wonder what they taste like.

This is quite pleasant . . .

. . . but the view is better from here.

What's happening next door?

She said she'd only be five minutes . . .

Come on, open that door!

They'll never eat all this fruit.

Isn't that my blanket?

I'll just have to sleep on here instead.

I'm not sure I really like this.

Nearly time for some proper food.

I just can't settle tonight . . .

. . . there's too much going on.

I don't think I should have done that.

I was only trying to help.

What am I supposed to do with this?

I much prefer the box.

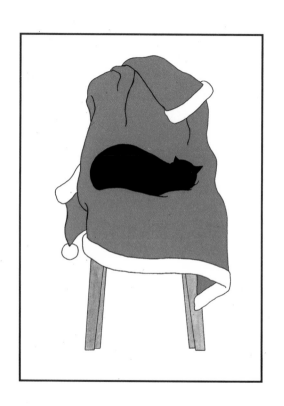